SERVICE-LEARNING

PLANNING AND REFLECTION

A Step-by-Step Guide

Anika Knox

David B. Wangaard

Sandra R. Michaelson

Student Name: _____

The School for Ethical Education
440 Wheelers Farms Road
Milford, CT 06460
Phone: (203) 783-4438 or (800) 232-0013 ext. 4438
Fax: (203) 783-4461
E-mail: ethics@ethicsed.org
Web site: www.ethicsed.org

ISBN: 1-892056-29-1

For ordering copies of this resource, contact:

Character Development Group
P.O. Box 9211
Chapel Hill, NC 27515-9211
Phone: **919.967.2110**
Fax: **919.967.2139**
E-mail: **Respect96@aol.com**
www.**CharacterEducation.com**

Acknowledgements

This guide is an outgrowth of The School for Ethical Education's *Youth: Ethics in Service (YES)* program, which began in 1998. As this service-earning program developed, it became clear that one thing was missing. Despite all the wonderful service projects the teams were doing, students were having a hard time planning and reflecting on their projects in a meaningful way. We put our heads together and came up with an idea: to create a guide that students and adults can use to plan and reflect on their project through an ethical lens.

We wish to thank the students, teachers, group leaders, and evaluators who have made our *Youth: Ethics in Service (YES)* program and this guide possible. We are also grateful to the following organizations for their generous support of our efforts: The Louis Calder Foundation; State of Connecticut Department of Education, Learn and Serve program; Greater Bridgeport Area Foundation; The Community Foundation of Southeastern Connecticut; and Wright Investors' Service.

Table of Contents

Congratulations on your decision to do a service-learning project! Service-learning projects give you the opportunity to be heroic and do something meaningful. This guide will help you come up with a a project idea, plan a project, reflect on your work, work well as a team, and demonstrate good character.

We encourage adults and students to use this guide together. This will make the project more meaningful to all. This guide is made up of two parts. Part 1, Project Planning, will help you plan a project. You do not need to be an expert in service-learning or even have a project idea in mind to begin this guide. The important thing is to work together to find, plan, do, and reflect on a service-learning project.

Be sure to complete Part 1 before you begin your project. This will give you a solid foundation for your project. Also, complete the pages in this section in order. You may be working as a team, but be sure that each student completes his or her own project pages.

Part 2 of this guide is Project Reflection. These pages will help you reflect on (think about) the experiences you have throughout your project. Here are some tips about how to use Part 2:

• It is best to reflect frequently and consistently. The more reflection activities you do, the more you will get out of your experience. There are enough journal entries for you to complete one per week throughout an entire school year.

• Reflection exercises are more meaningful when there is group follow-up and discussion.

• The reflection pages do not need to be completed in any particular order, although some pages should only be completed after you have completed your project.

• Journal entries can be completed during class or club time or as a homework assignment.

• Some people find it easier to draw their responses than to write them. We've included entries that allow you to choose to express your reflections artistically.

At the end of the guide are personalized pages for reflection, notes, and ideas. Feel free to use these pages to come up with your own reflection questions. We have also included pages to help you keep track of the time you spend on your service project.

We hope that you have a wonderful service experience. If you are interested in learning more about service-learning and reflection and other programs of The School for Ethical Education, please visit our Web site at www.ethicsed.org.

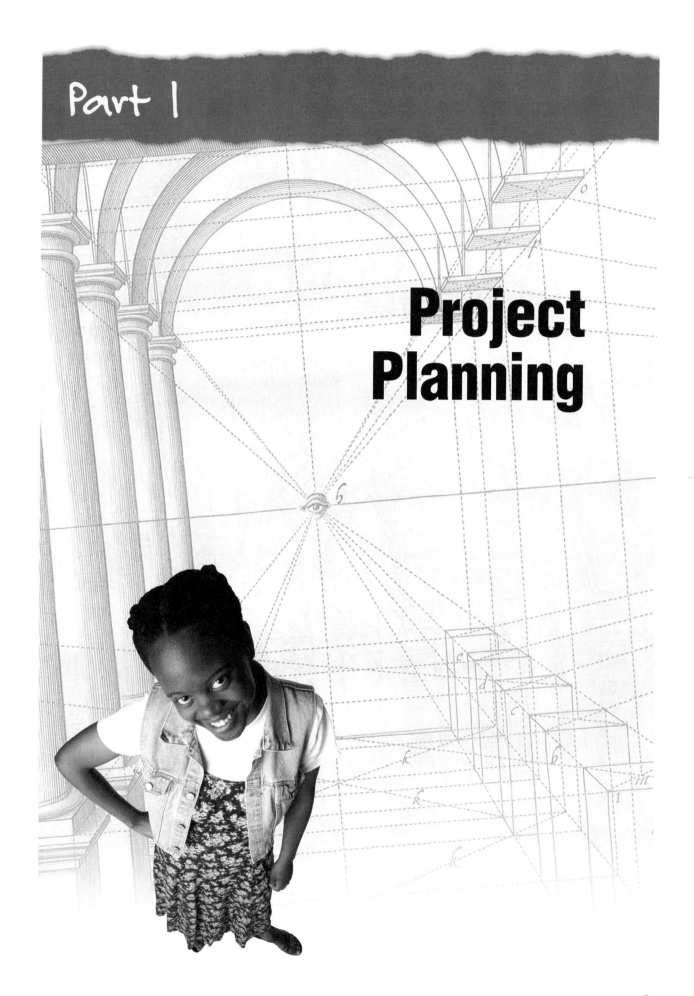

Part 1

Project Planning

The Basics

Service-Learning

Students learn while doing a needed community service project.

FOUR STEPS TO EVERY SERVICE-LEARNING PROJECT

PREPARATION
- Find community need
- Research community need
- Plan the project
- Identify and develop team skills

ACTION
- Do project
- Advertise project
- Tell your story

REFLECTION
- Journal writing
- Reading and discussion
- Talking with others
- Artistic expression

CELEBRATION
- Parties
- Assemblies
- Certificates
- Thank you cards

THREE TYPES OF SERVICE-LEARNING PROJECTS

DIRECT
Working directly with the people or things you help (for example, visiting senior citizens or reading to children)

INDIRECT
Helping people or things but not working directly with them (for example, food drives)

ADVOCACY
Researching, telling, writing, and educating people on a issue to help solve a problem (for example, creating brochures or videos)

FOUR SERVICE-LEARNING TOPICS

EDUCATION
Examples:
- tutoring programs
- mentoring programs
- reading to the young

ENVIRONMENT
Examples:
- recycling projects
- clean-ups
- habitat restoration

HUMAN NEEDS
Examples:
- working with senior citizens, hospitals, shelters and soup kitchens

PUBLIC SAFETY
Examples:
- health fairs
- peer-mediation programs

The Community You Serve

There are many communities a project can serve. A community is not just your neighborhood. A community can be your classroom, your school, your state, your country, or the world!

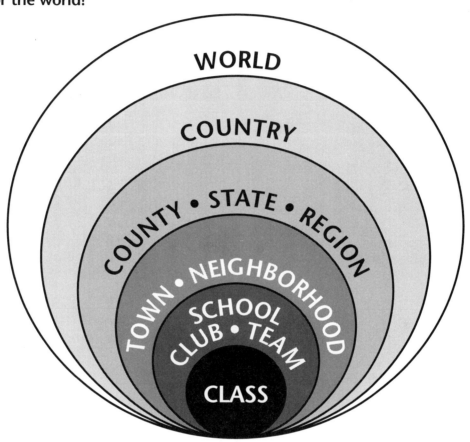

There are many people and things you can help in a community. These people and things are called service recipients.

Individual people	Animals	Hospitals	Animal shelters
Food banks	Neighborhoods	Museums	Libraries
Students in your grade	Groups of people (babies, senior citizens, poor people in another country)	Nature preserves	Immigrants
Students in another grade		Senior centers	Parks
		Preschools	

Needs and Resources

As a team, identify two to three communities in which you might choose to complete a service-learning project. Brainstorm needs that you see in each community, resources that might help reduce the needs, and service-project ideas your team could complete.

Community	Needs	Resources	Project Ideas
Examples: your class, school, local youth club, neighborhood, town, county, state	Examples: students could be helped by peer tutors, a youth-club needs additional athletic equipment, a senior center has few visitors	People, money, tools, talents. Examples: students are willing to help younger students, parent works for sporting goods store, school is in walking distance of senior center	Examples: create peer tutoring service, organize fund-raiser for youth-center with advocacy for healthy activities, organize visits to senior center with goal to obtain direct accounts of local historical events

Does your team need to do more research on needs and resources? Where can you go for information? Try asking school staff and parents or using libraries, newspapers, town government, the Internet...

Character Survey

This survey can help identify personal character traits that team members can choose to demonstrate.

1. Circle three character traits you believe are important for people to demonstrate when working together. Use a dictionary to look up any character traits you do not know. Add other character traits not listed here that are important to you.

Character Traits

Caring	Courage	Honesty	Patience
Cheerfulness	Courtesy	Initiative	Perseverance
Citizenship	Dependability	Love	Respect
Confidence	Fairness	Loyalty	Responsibility
Cooperation	Generosity	Optimism	Other_____

2. In the following box, pick one of the traits you circled and write down how you can show or not show this trait. Be specific. For example, courtesy can be shown when you hold the door for someone.

Character trait:_____

is shown when _____

is *not* shown when _____

3. Why is it important to think about character traits and behavior when you work on a service project?

_____

_____

_____

Remember the character traits you chose and remind yourself throughout your project to demonstrate the traits you believe are important.

Planning and Reflection, A Step-by-Step Guide   7

Character at Work

Make sure you complete page 7 before doing this activity. This is an activity for your whole team.

In this activity you will discover three character traits that your *entire team* shares. Your team's goal can be to demonstrate these traits throughout your project.

Step 1: Choose someone to be the note taker (recorder) and record responses on the board or on paper. Make sure everyone can see the responses.

Step 2: Go around the room and have each student—and your adult leader—list their top three character traits from page 7. Each time someone mentions a character trait, add it to the list and put a check mark next to it. Put a check mark next to that trait each time it is mentioned after that. For example, if five people choose honesty as one of their top three traits, the recorder should put five check marks next to honesty.

Step 3: Add up all the check marks to find the top three character traits for your team.

Step 4: Create a poster of these character traits.

As a team, come to agreement (find consensus) on examples of each character trait.

1. Character trait: _____

   is shown when _____

   _____

   _____

   is not shown when _____

2. Character trait: _____

   is shown when _____

   _____

   _____

   is not shown when _____

3. Character trait: _____

   is shown when _____

   _____

   _____

   is not shown when _____

SERVICE-LEARNING

Team Roles

Each person in the team should choose a team role. More than one person in a group can share a role. Here are some suggested team roles and their responsibilities. Your team may decide to rotate roles from time to time.

Leader Keeps team motivated Assigns what needs to get done Makes sure job duties are understood	**Timekeeper** Keeps track of time during meetings Makes sure there is time to reflect Keeps track of project deadlines
Recorder Summarizes team meetings Creates meeting agenda Keeps a team project log	**Balancer** Makes sure all members are participating Makes sure jobs are evenly distributed Takes the lead in resolving team conflicts
Reporter/Public Relations Gets other people interested in the project Creates advertising for project Updates new/absent members on project	**Reflecter** Leads reflection sessions Asks questions of the team Leads team evaluation of the project

1. How do you think team roles could help your service team? Be specific.

_____

_____

_____

2. Which team role would you enjoy? Why?

_____

_____

_____

Cero a Cinco

Cero a Cinco allows everyone to vote on an idea, but also allows all team members to explain why they voted a certain way. This helps all team members feel that their votes matter and reach a team consensus.

Here is how *Cero a Cinco* works:

1. Someone brings up a choice or an idea, and the team leader calls for a vote by *Cero a Cinco*. Each person then holds up zero to five fingers according to how they feel about the choice or idea.

   - **Five (cinco) fingers** shows that you strongly support the idea.
   - **Four (cuatro) fingers** lets people know you would like to suggest one change.
   - **Three (tres) fingers** shows you agree but you have more than a few changes to suggest.
   - **Two (dos) fingers** lets people know you think the idea could work but you feel it needs lots of changes (you should have ideas for those changes).
   - **One (uno) finger** means you disagree with the idea but are willing to work to make the idea better.
   - **Zero (cero) fingers** lets people know that you strongly disagree and have serious problems with the choice or idea and believe it should be dropped.

2. Have the team recorder tally how many team members raised *cinco* (5), *cuatro* (4), *tres* (3), *dos* (2), *uno* (1), or *cero* (0) fingers.

3. Has your team reached a consensus? (This can be when most team members have raised *tres*, *cuatro*, or *cinco* fingers. Consensus does not have to be 100 percent agreement.) If there is a consensus, move forward with that idea.

4. If your team has not reached a consensus, have the team leader ask those who raised *cero*, *uno*, *dos*, or *tres* fingers to describe their ideas or concerns. Ask, *Why did you put up ___ fingers, and what changes can we make that would make you want to hold up* quatro *or* cinco *fingers?* If it would be helpful, create a new idea that includes suggestions from your team members.

5. Repeat steps 1–4 until your team has reached a comfortable consensus.

As a team, try practicing *Cero a Cinco* with this idea:

For our next meeting, everyone will bring an orange for a team snack.

Did your team reach a consensus in the first vote? Did team members make suggestions to improve the idea?

Now that you have worked on ways to be successful as a team, it's time to put them to work on your project planning!

Choosing a Community

Take your team's ideas from page 5 and use *Cero a Cinco* to choose a community to serve. Move forward with the community that has the greatest consensus. Remember, your team can create a new idea for a community that uses team members' suggestions.

Community Idea 1: _____

Number of fingers for Community Idea 1:

Cinco (5) _____ *Cuatro* (4) _____ *Tres* (3) _____ *Dos* (2) _____ *Uno* (1) _____ *Cero* (0) _____

Suggestions and/or concerns for Community Idea 1:

_____

_____

Community Idea 2: _____

Number of fingers for Community Idea 2:

Cinco (5) _____ *Cuatro* (4) _____ *Tres* (3) _____ *Dos* (2) _____ *Uno* (1) _____ *Cero* (0) _____

Suggestions and/or concerns for Community Idea 2:

_____

_____

Community Idea 3: _____

Number of fingers for Community Idea 3:

Cinco (5) _____ *Cuatro* (4) _____ *Tres* (3) _____ *Dos* (2) _____ *Uno* (1) _____ *Cero* (0) _____

Suggestions and/or concerns for Community Idea 3:

_____

_____

Community Idea 4: _____

Number of fingers for Community Idea 4:

Cinco (5) _____ *Cuatro* (4) _____ *Tres* (3) _____ *Dos* (2) _____ *Uno* (1) _____ *Cero* (0) _____

Suggestions and/or concerns for Community Idea 4:

_____

_____

Which community has the greatest consensus? _____

Congratulations! Your team has chosen a community to serve!

Project Tree

Write the community your team has chosen to serve on the line below (from page 11).

_____

Write the people, groups, or things your project will serve (service recipients) on the line below.

_____

Describe three project ideas that could help the service recipients.
These ideas can come from the table you completed on page 6.

Project Idea 1:

_____

_____

_____

Project Idea 2:

_____

_____

_____

Project Idea 3:

_____

_____

_____

SERVICE-LEARNING

Deciding What To Do

Use Cero a Cinco to help select a project idea.

Take your team's ideas from page 12 and use *Cero a Cinco* to choose a project. Move forward with the project that has the greatest consensus. Remember, your team can create a new idea for a project that uses team members' suggestions.

Project Idea 1: _____

Number of fingers for Project Idea 1:

Cinco (5) _____ *Cuatro* (4) _____ *Tres* (3) _____ *Dos* (2) _____ *Uno* (1) _____ *Cero* (0) _____

Suggestions and/or concerns for Project Idea 1:

_____

_____

Project Idea 2: _____

Number of fingers for Project Idea 2:

Cinco (5) _____ *Cuatro* (4) _____ *Tres* (3) _____ *Dos* (2) _____ *Uno* (1) _____ *Cero* (0) _____

Suggestions and/or concerns for Project Idea 2:

_____

_____

Project Idea 3: _____

Number of fingers for Project Idea 3:

Cinco (5) _____ *Cuatro* (4) _____ *Tres* (3) _____ *Dos* (2) _____ *Uno* (1) _____ *Cero* (0) _____

Suggestions and/or concerns for Project Idea 3:

_____

_____

Project Idea 4: _____

Number of fingers for Project Idea 4:

Cinco (5) _____ *Cuatro* (4) _____ *Tres* (3) _____ *Dos* (2) _____ *Uno* (1) _____ *Cero* (0) _____

Suggestions and/or concerns for Project Idea 4:

_____

_____

Which project has the greatest consensus? _____

Congratulations! Your team has chosen a project!

Project Outline

Community to Be Served (from page 11): _____

Project Idea (from page 13): Briefly describe the project you have chosen and the needs this project will meet. _____

_____

_____

Project Goals: Clearly state what will be accomplished if your project is successful, including team goals such as working well together, having fun.

_____

_____

Learning Goals: What school or club learning objectives will be met during this project?
Participants will _____

_____

_____

_____

Project Title: Give your project a title. Try to be creative, brief, and clear. Your title may be used to build team identity, for publicity, on team T-shirts...

_____

Preparation Steps

What Do We Need to Know?

Identify the questions you need to answer to begin your project. Examples: Do we need anyone's approval to begin this project? Do we need any help with transportation, and how much will transportation cost? Do we need to learn new skills to complete our project?

_____

_____

_____

_____

_____

Project Outline *continued*

Getting the Answers

Identify where you can get answers to your project questions and assign team members to do the research necessary to bring back answers for your team. In each box, identify a question and the team member who will research the answer.

Library Question: Researcher:	School Staff (principal, secretary, counselor...) Question: Researcher:	Community Organization (Boys & Girls Club, senior center...) Question: Researcher:
Survey/Interview Question: Researcher:	Internet Question: Researcher:	Business Question: Researcher:
Local Government (Rec department, mayor's office...) Question: Researcher:	Other _____ Question: Researcher:	Other _____ Question: Researcher:

Resource Check

Summarize the resources you have (from page 6) and identify the resources you will need to complete your project. Brainstorm ideas about how to obtain additional resources that are needed.

Resources We Have (from page 6) Examples: people, money, tools, talent	Resources We Need Examples: support, approval, supplies, training	Ideas to Obtain Resources Examples: support from PTA, grant from local business or foundation, parents, fundraising

Project Outline *continued*

Identifying Project Tasks

1. As a team, brainstorm the tasks that need to be done to complete your project successfully.

2. Team members should volunteer or be assigned to each task. Some tasks can be completed by more than one team member.

3. Select a date for completion of each task.

4. Have the team recorder create a list of these tasks, who is assigned to each task, and when each task is due. Make sure that everyone has this list or display it in your classroom.

5. Individual team members should use the table below for the tasks they will complete.

6. Review all of the tasks and the steps needed to complete them with your adult leader. Revise if necessary.

7. Keep track of your assignments and be sure to check them off once you have completed them!

Project Tasks (Include specific steps needed to complete each task.)	Team Member(s) Assigned to Task	Task Due Date
Example: Create a permission slip for travel to senior center. The permission slip will be ready to copy and will be attractive, accurate, and free of errors.	Mike, Samantha	Draft - 9/20 Final - 9/27

Project Outline *continued*

Telling Our Story

Brainstorm ways your team can communicate stories about and lessons learned from your project. Add this job to the team assignment list. Examples: bulletin board, oral report to parents, school assembly, presentation to school board, school or club Web site, press release, pamphlet, school or club newspaper.

Our team will tell our story by

_____

_____

_____

_____

_____

Celebrate!

It is fun and important to celebrate the completion of good work. Service-learning projects create challenges to overcome and opportunities to celebrate perseverance and success. When you overcome a challenge or complete your project, don't forget to celebrate.

Celebration should acknowledge work well done, help to build a sense of positive teamwork, help recruit others to future service, and balance work and fun. Use this celebration checklist to create your own celebration plan.

- ☐ Celebration includes all participants
- ☐ Planning considers location, expense, other events scheduled at same time
- ☐ All team members contribute to celebration
- ☐ Celebration includes food
- ☐ Invitations include people who helped team

- ☐ Certificates of completion or awards are provided
- ☐ Fun activity is planned
- ☐ Cleanup is planned
- ☐ Say thank you a lot

Celebration Plan

_____

_____

_____

_____

_____

Congratulations! You have completed your project planning. The next section of this guide will help you reflect, evaluate, record your service hours, and jot down notes and ideas. We wish you great success and hope you learn and have fun during your service-learning project.

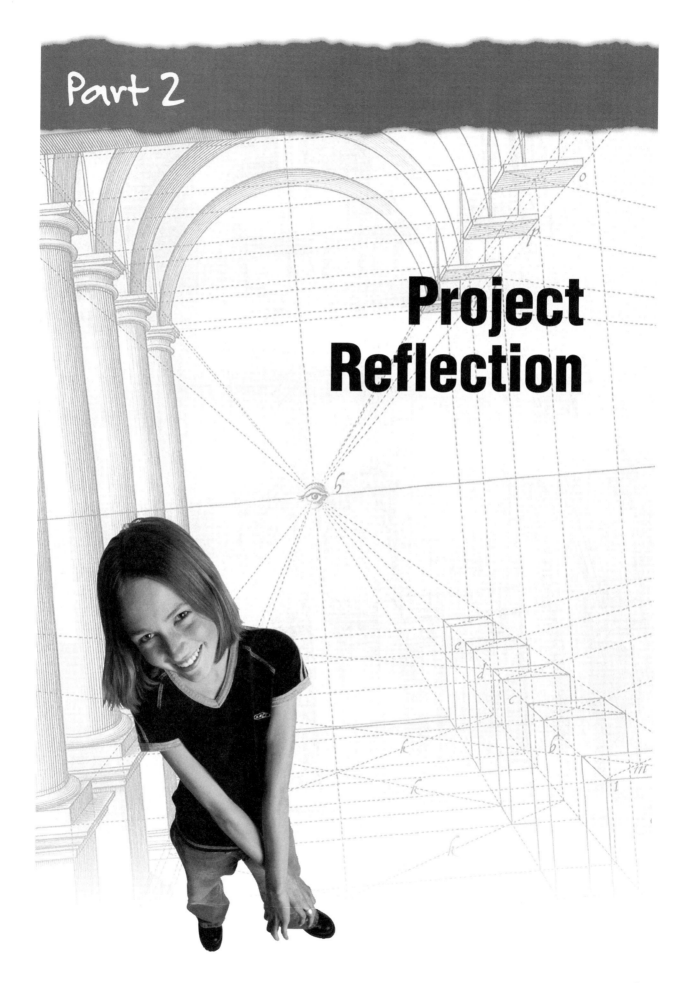

Part 2

Project Reflection

Introduction to Reflection

An important part of service-learning is reflection. Writing is a wonderful way to reflect and think about your service-learning experience. Read the information below before you begin the reflection portion of this guide.

What is reflection?

Reflection means thinking about your past, present, or future experiences. This guide will help you reflect on things you encounter during your service project. The questions will also help you to think about what you have learned from your service project. With such busy lives, you do not often get a chance to sit back and think about your ideas, feelings, actions, hopes, and dreams. This section was created to give you a chance to just think.

You will be asked to write, draw, or work with others to reflect on your service project. The reflection questions can help you focus on improving your project. The reflection portion of this guide will also help you think about making decisions.

How should I use the reflection portion of this guide?

Work with your adult leader to decide on the best way to complete the reflection pages. Feel free to respond to the same entry more than once or to add to an entry you started earlier.

Try to complete *at least* one reflection activity every week. Use ideas, beliefs, and experiences from all parts of your life—not only from your service project. You or your adult leader can even create personalized reflection questions on pages 62-65.

What can I write?

Write freely, but remember that others may read your reflections. Be honest and thoughtful, and think before you write. Write as much as you are able. You may fill an entire page on one day and write only a few sentences the next. Above all else, HAVE FUN! This journal should not be a chore. Try to write or draw as neatly as you can, but don't worry about every mistake.

Ways to Reflect

How do I reflect?

There are many ways to focus your reflection. In this guide we suggest three.

Wide Angle: When you reflect in the wide-angle mode, think about the big picture of your experience. For example, if you are working at a soup kitchen for your project, you might reflect on the issue of hunger and why there isn't enough food for everyone.

Microscope: When you reflect in the microscope mode, think about the details of your experience. For example, if you are working at a soup kitchen for your project, you might reflect on how you can work with other people to collect and donate the food.

Mirror: When you reflect in the mirror mode, think about your own actions and beliefs. For example, if you are working at a soup kitchen for your project, you might reflect on how you would feel if you were hungry and needed help.

What can I do to reflect?

There are four basic reflection categories. They are:

Writing: essays, journals, guides for future volunteers, advertisements, articles, songs

Speaking: in small groups, in large groups, one-on-one, oral reports

Activities: role-play, teach others, create a puppet show, hold a celebration party

Drama and Art: photo essays, paintings, drawings, collages, dances

This guide will give you opportunities to practice these types of reflection.

Solving Problems

Do you believe that it is only the responsibility of "experts" to solve problems in your community? Why or why not?

_____

_____

_____

_____

_____

_____

_____

_____

_____

_____

_____

_____

_____

_____

_____

_____

_____

_____

_____

_____

_____

_____

_____

Project Importance

Why is this project important to you?

_____

_____

_____

_____

_____

_____

_____

_____

_____

_____

_____

_____

_____

_____

_____

_____

_____

_____

_____

_____

_____

Good Stuff

What do you like about this project? Draw and/or write your response.

Project Poetry

Write a poem about your project. Use the format below or create your own poem.

A suggestion for a poem format	Example using the format at left
(project title)	We care
(project goal)	To help the homeless
(2 adjectives that describe the project)	Needed and interesting
Helping (describe who you are helping)	Helping to give food to the shelter
I believe in (2 character traits)	I believe in caring and respect.
I am (your name) and (one thing about you)	I am Joe Morgan and am glad to serve.

EXTRA!! Turn your poem into lyrics for a song. Use a tune you already know or create your own.

Differences

Do you enjoy being around people whose backgrounds and experiences are different from yours? Why or why not?

_____

_____

_____

_____

_____

_____

_____

_____

_____

_____

_____

_____

_____

_____

_____

_____

_____

_____

_____

_____

_____

_____

_____

The Golden Rule

The Golden Rule says to treat other people as you would like to be treated. **Why is the Golden Rule important?**

_____

_____

_____

_____

_____

_____

_____

_____

_____

Can you remember a time in your life when you demonstrated or saw someone demonstrate the Golden Rule? Explain. If not, think of a situation that would give you a chance to practice the Golden Rule. Describe or sketch the situation.

Working Together

Are the members of your team working well together? Explain. As you answer, think about the character traits and the team roles described earlier. If you are not working in a team, explain how well you've worked with others in the past.

_____

_____

_____

_____

_____

_____

_____

_____

_____

_____

_____

_____

_____

_____

_____

_____

_____

_____

_____

_____

_____

EXTRA!! With other team members, act out in a skit positive character traits you have seen team members demonstrate during your project work.

SERVICE-LEARNING

The Time Is Now

"How wonderful it is that nobody need wait a single moment before starting to improve the world."

—Anne Frank

What does this quote mean to you?

_____

_____

_____

_____

_____

_____

_____

_____

_____

_____

_____

_____

_____

_____

_____

_____

_____

_____

_____

_____

_____

Changing the Future

I believe that I can change what might happen tomorrow by what I do today.

Do you agree or disagree with this statement? Agree_____ Disagree_____

What do you think? _____

_____

_____

_____

_____

_____

_____

_____

_____

_____

_____

_____

_____

_____

_____

_____

_____

_____

_____

_____

_____

_____

Stronger Character

Are there any character traits you would like to strengthen? Use the list of character traits on page 7 to help you. For example, you may admire the fact that you are a cheerful and respectful person, but would like to work on being more patient. What does this character trait mean? How could you show it?

_____

_____

_____

_____

_____

_____

_____

_____

_____

_____

_____

_____

_____

_____

_____

_____

_____

_____

_____

_____

_____

Understanding the Need

What problem or need does your project address (for example, homelessness, illiteracy, or hunger)? Why is this problem or need important to you? Write and/or draw your answer.

What caused the problem or need that your project addresses? Explain. If you don't know, how can you find out?

_____

_____

_____

_____

_____

_____

_____

_____

_____

_____

_____

_____

_____

SERVICE-LEARNING

How Do I Decide?
Decision-Making Steps

Throughout your project—and your life— you will have to make tough decisions. These steps can help you.

1. Ask yourself, *Is there a decision to make?* Ask yourself, *What choices do I have?*

2. What character traits do you want to demonstrate as you make your decision? Ask yourself, *Do my choices follow the Golden Rule?* (Look back to page 27 to review the Golden Rule.)

3. Make a decision and act on it.

4. Later, reflect on the outcome of your choice.

The following story will help you practice the first three decision-making steps above. Read the story and then use these steps to think about and answer the questions below.

Your class is meeting on a Friday afternoon and reflecting on activities for your service project. Nearly everyone has agreed on most of the ideas, and you are all ready to go home for the weekend. Just then, one of your classmates suggests another idea. He usually doesn't participate in class, and he gets picked on a lot in school. You think his idea is really good, but the rest of the class laughs and says it is stupid. The boy sits back, crosses his arms, and doesn't say anything. Should you do anything?

1. Is there a decision to make? What is it, and what are your choices?

_____
_____
_____

2. What character trait(s) do you think should guide you as you make this decision?

_____
_____
_____

3. Do your choices follow the Golden Rule?

_____
_____
_____

4. What would you decide to do?

_____
_____
_____

Planning and Reflection, A Step-by-Step Guide

33

What Works

What is working well on this project?

_____

_____

_____

_____

_____

_____

_____

_____

_____

_____

_____

_____

_____

_____

_____

_____

_____

_____

_____

_____

_____

_____

_____

SERVICE-LEARNING

Getting to Know You

Describe one person you have gotten to know during your service project. What positive things (talents, skills, character traits) have you learned from or about this person? Write and/or draw your answer.

Learning Beyond School

Service-learning projects help students link what they learn in school to real life. Does your project do this? How?

_____
_____
_____
_____
_____
_____
_____
_____
_____

What are you learning through this project?

_____
_____
_____
_____
_____
_____
_____
_____
_____

To the Max

Have you been trying your hardest during the project? Explain. If not, what could you do differently?

_____

_____

_____

_____

_____

_____

_____

_____

_____

_____

_____

_____

_____

_____

_____

_____

_____

_____

_____

_____

_____

_____

_____

_____

Making a Difference

"We should be paid for helping others."

Do you agree with this statement? Yes_____ No_____

What do you think? _____

_____

_____

_____

_____

_____

_____

_____

_____

_____

_____

_____

_____

_____

_____

_____

_____

_____

_____

_____

_____

SERVICE-LEARNING

Meeting the Challenge

What have been your greatest personal challenges during the project? How have you handled them?

_____

_____

_____

_____

_____

_____

_____

_____

_____

_____

_____

_____

_____

_____

_____

_____

_____

_____

_____

_____

_____

Remember the character traits you chose and ask yourself throughout your project if you are demonstrating the traits you believe are important.

Moving Mountains

Have you or your team run into a problem or an obstacle during your project?

1. Describe the obstacle or problem in detail.

_____

_____

_____

_____

_____

_____

2. List the resources (people, skills, tools, money) you used or could use to help you solve the problem. Next to each resource, explain how it helped or could help.

_____

_____

_____

_____

_____

_____

3. Were you able to solve the problem? Would you do anything differently if you encountered this problem again?

_____

_____

_____

_____

_____

_____

SERVICE-LEARNING

Required or Voluntary?

Shoud students be required to perform service projects to graduate from school?

Yes _____   No _____   Sometimes _____

What do you think? _____

_____

_____

_____

_____

_____

_____

_____

_____

_____

_____

_____

_____

_____

_____

_____

_____

_____

_____

_____

_____

_____

_____

Chores and Choices
Ethical Decision Making

Sometimes decisions require us to make choices about friends, honesty, and loyalty.

Your friends are getting together after school and ask you to come with them. Your parents have given you a list of chores to do by the end of the day. You really want to go with your friends, but you know you won't be able to get your chores done if you go with them. You also know that your parents are trusting you to do the chores.

1. Is there a decision to make? What is it, and what are your choices?

_____

_____

_____

_____

2. What character traits(s) do you think should guide you as you make this decision?

_____

_____

_____

_____

3. Do your choices follow the Golden Rule?

_____

_____

_____

_____

4. What would you decide to do?

_____

_____

_____

_____

SERVICE-LEARNING

Reflect on Reflecting

How has reflection been helpful to you or to your class? Explain by writing and/or drawing.

Remember the character traits you chose and ask yourself throughout your project if you are demonstrating the traits you believe are important.

You Won't Believe This

What is the funniest or most surprising thing that has happened so far on this project? Write about it, show it in a drawing, or create a skit about it with others.

The More, The Merrier

"Many hands make light work." —English proverb

Do you agree with this statement? Yes_____ No_____

What do you think? _____

_____

_____

_____

_____

_____

_____

_____

_____

_____

_____

_____

_____

_____

_____

_____

_____

_____

_____

Remember the character traits you chose and ask yourself throughout your project if you are demonstrating the traits you believe are important.

Extra! Extra!

What would you like others to know about this project? Make a list of these things. Go back to page 17 and use this list to tell your story.

SERVICE-LEARNING

Cleaning Up

What could be done to improve your project? Create a list of ideas.

_____

_____

_____

_____

_____

_____

_____

_____

_____

_____

_____

_____

_____

_____

_____

_____

_____

_____

_____

_____

_____

_____

EXTRA!! Share these ideas with your team and try some of them.

Honor System
Ethical Decision Making

Rarely does a decision affect only you.

To get a passing grade in one of your classes, you must complete 30 hours of service. It is the end of April, and you have completed only 15 hours at the animal shelter where you chose to volunteer. However, lately you haven't had time to go to the shelter. If you don't complete the 15 hours in the next month, you will not pass the class.

You realize you can lie to your teacher about the number of the hours you have completed without anyone knowing. If you record 10 extra hours, you will only have to complete five hours during the next month. You have time to do five more hours.

1. Is there a decision to make? What is it, and what choices do you have?

_____

_____

_____

_____

2. What character trait(s) do you think should guide you as you make this decision?

_____

_____

_____

_____

3. Do your choices follow the Golden Rule?

_____

_____

_____

_____

4. What would you decide to do?

_____

_____

_____

_____

Making Changes

Have you ever had to make a change that was difficult? Explain by writing and/or drawing how you made the change and what the outcome was.

Self-Discovery

Have you discovered character traits or skills you didn't realize you had before you started the project? Explain and give examples.

_____

_____

_____

_____

_____

_____

_____

_____

_____

_____

_____

_____

_____

_____

_____

_____

_____

_____

_____

_____

The Choice Is Yours
Ethical Decision Making

You are walking home alone when you notice a group of kids from school ahead of you. You realize they are teasing a kid from your class named Beth. Beth doesn't have many friends, and people are mean to her. Usually, she just ignores them and walks away, but you can't believe that it doesn't bother her. You don't see why people pick on her so much. As you get closer, you realize that some of the kids in the group are friends of yours. You are in front of your house now and the other kids are less than a block away.

1. Is there a decision to make? What is it, and what are your choices?

_____

_____

_____

_____

2. What character trait(s) do you think should guide you as you make this decision?

_____

_____

_____

_____

3. Do your choices follow the Golden Rule?

_____

_____

_____

_____

4. What would you decide to do?

_____

_____

_____

_____

Making Connections

Would you like to stay involved with the people or things you helped through your project after your project is completed? Why or why not? How could you stay involved?

_____

_____

_____

_____

_____

_____

_____

_____

_____

_____

_____

_____

_____

_____

_____

_____

_____

_____

_____

_____

_____

_____

People Person

Has your project experience changed the way you work with other people? Explain.

Examples: You now enjoy working in groups, you learned how to speak in public, or you became more patient.

_____

_____

_____

_____

_____

_____

_____

_____

_____

_____

_____

_____

_____

_____

_____

_____

_____

_____

_____

_____

_____

_____

Let Me Tell You

What advice do you have for people who do service projects in the future?

_____

_____

_____

_____

_____

_____

_____

_____

_____

_____

_____

_____

_____

_____

_____

_____

_____

_____

_____

_____

_____

_____

_____

SERVICE-LEARNING

That's Better

Do you think your project made a difference? List all the positive things that happened because of your project. Answer this question after your project has been completed.

_____

_____

_____

_____

_____

_____

_____

_____

_____

_____

_____

_____

_____

_____

_____

_____

_____

_____

_____

_____

_____

Time's Up

Did you and your team get the project done on time? How could you or your group have managed time better? Answer this question after you complete your project.

_____

_____

_____

_____

_____

_____

_____

_____

_____

_____

_____

_____

_____

_____

_____

_____

_____

_____

Remember the character traits you chose and ask yourself throughout your project if you are demonstrating the traits you believe are important.

Thinking Ahead

Can you think of another service project you would like to do in the future either at home or at school? Write about it, sketch it, or cut pictures out of a newspaper or a magazine.

Making the Grade

Microscope

NAME OF TEAM AND PROJECT: _____

✓+ Excellent   ✓ Average   ✓- Poor

GRADE	SUBJECT	REASONS FOR GRADE
	Preparation	
	Action	
	Reflection	
	Celebration	
	Practicing Good Character	
	Working Together & Consensus Building	
	Making Decisions	

SERVICE-LEARNING

Who Are You Now?

Has the project experience changed the way you feel about yourself? Explain by writing or drawing below. Answer this question after you complete your project.

Celebrate!

List all the things you can celebrate about your project. Then, with your team or class, use *Cero a Cinco* to decide on three things to celebrate. Agree on one or two and then celebrate them! Take a look back at page 17 to help you plan your celebration.

Things to celebrate:

_____

_____

_____

_____

_____

Use *Cero a Cinco* to decide on three things to celebrate:

1. _____

2. _____

3. _____

The Big Think

Congratulations! You have completed the journal. Think back on all the journal questions you answered and the skills you learned. Write or draw your final thoughts.

Personalized Reflection

SERVICE-LEARNING

Personalized Reflection

Personalized Reflection

Personalized Reflection

Keeping Track

Keep track of the amount of time you spend on your project. Track the time you spend planning, doing, reflecting, and celebrating. All these hours count! The first entry is an example.

Date & Amount of Time	Activities Done	Date & Amount of Time	Activities Done
January 5 25 minutes	We worked together in groups to make greeting cards and then spent time reflecting.		

SERVICE-LEARNING

Keeping Track

Date & Amount of Time	Activities Done

Date & Amount of Time	Activities Done

Keeping Track

Date & Amount of Time	Activities Done

Date & Amount of Time	Activities Done

SERVICE-LEARNING

Notes and Ideas

The next several pages are designed for you to write notes, ideas, contacts, and just things you want to remember about your project. Write whatever comes to mind; you may not use it now, but it may be useful later.

_____
_____
_____
_____
_____
_____
_____
_____
_____
_____
_____
_____
_____
_____
_____
_____
_____
_____
_____
_____
_____

Notes and Ideas

_____

_____

_____

_____

_____

_____

_____

_____

_____

_____

_____

_____

_____

_____

_____

_____

_____

_____

_____

_____

_____

_____

_____

_____

_____

_____

Notes and Ideas

_____
_____
_____
_____
_____
_____
_____
_____
_____
_____
_____
_____
_____
_____
_____
_____
_____
_____
_____
_____
_____
_____
_____

Glossary

Below are terms used throughout this guide.
Below are terms used throughout this guide.

Character—*Moral or ethical traits, abilities, or attributes*
Examples of character include honesty, respect, responsibility.
"He demonstrated good character by helping others."

Consensus—*An opinion of most of a group; general agreement*
An example of a way to reach consensus is to use *Cero a Cinco* (see page 10).
"To reach consensus on a project to do, we have to hear everyone's opinion."

Goal—*The object that effort is directed toward*
"The goal of our project is to cheer up sick children."

Golden Rule—*Treat others the way you would like to be treated.*
"If I think about the Golden Rule before I act, I will usually make better choices."

Reflection—*The act of thinking about past, present, or future experiences*
"Our reflection meetings help us think about our actions and experiences during the project."

Service—*The act of giving assistance*
"Service is an important part of growing up. We should all try to help."

Service-Learning—*Acquiring or using new knowledge or skills by helping someone or something.*
"We want our service-learning project this year to deal with human needs and education. We will tutor younger students."

Team Roles—*Jobs or assignments given to members of a team*
"When we use team roles, our team works together better."

SERVICE-LEARNING

For additional character education resources, contact:

P.O. Box 9211
Chapel Hill, NC 27515-9211
Phone: 919.967.2110
Fax: 919.967.2139
E-mail: Respect96@aol.com

www.CharacterEducation.com